CW00847968

Out and About with Teddy Horsley

THE WALK   EXPLORER   NEIGHBOURS

by Leslie J Francis and Nicola M Slee
with pictures by Laura Cooper

published by Bible Society

The Bear facts

Teddy Horsley books are designed to build bridges between the young child's day to day experiences of the world and major biblical themes and stories.

Both authors work in church-linked colleges concerned with Teacher Education. Nicola Slee lectures in Religious Studies at Whitelands College in London. Leslie Francis is Research Fellow at Trinity College in Carmarthen.

Laura Cooper is a freelance children's illustrator working from Bristol. She has been engaged in art amongst groups of children and mentally handicapped adults.

The Teddy Horsley Series is a result of the authors' wide experience of educational work in schools and churches, and their extensive research into the religious development of young children.

"Out and About with Teddy Horsley" has previously been published as three separate stories:
The Walk   Explorer   Neighbours

BIBLE SOCIETY
Stonehill Green, Westlea, SWINDON SN5 7DG, England
Series editor: David Martin
Text © Leslie J Francis and Nicola M Slee 1990
Illustrations © Bible Society 1990

Unless otherwise stated, quotations from the Bible are from the Good News Bible, published by the Bible Societies/Harper Collins © American Bible Society, New York, 1966, 1971, 1976.

A catalogue record for this book is available from the British Library.

This edition published 1992. ISBN 0 564 08185X. Printed in Hong Kong.

The Walk

Betsy Bear senses God's Care

Betsy Bear likes to go walking with Mr and Mrs Henry, Lucy, Walter, and Teddy Horsley.

Sometimes they walk to the railway, where trains clatter past.

The guard tells Betsy where to stand so she will be safe.

Sometimes they walk in the country, where fields unfold for miles.

The farmer points out the signpost to Betsy
so she will not lose her way.

Sometimes they walk by the canal, where boats sway in the water.

The lock-keeper shows Betsy the path so she will not fall in.

Sometimes they walk in the park, where dogs chase and play.

The park-keeper stays close to Betsy's side so she will not get hurt.

Sometimes they walk in the town, where crowds and cars rush by.

The policewoman leads Betsy across the road
so the traffic will not harm her.

Sometimes they walk to the school,
where children run in the playground.

The teacher keeps an eye on Betsy so she will not get pushed over.

Everywhere she walks in the wide, wide world, Betsy Bear knows her friends are there to watch over her.

Betsy Bear likes to go walking with Mr and Mrs Henry, Lucy, Walter, and Teddy Horsley.

She hears the noisy trains zip past, but she is not afraid.

She sees the country lanes disappear into the distance,
but she knows she will not get lost.

She peers down into the deep water of the canal,
but she is not frightened.

She watches the playful dogs chase in the park,
but she knows she will not be harmed.

She feels the crowds push past her in the street,
but she does not worry.

She sees the children run and shout in school,
but she knows she is safe.

Everywhere she walks in the wide, wide world, Betsy Bear knows
God is there to watch over her.

In *The Walk,* Betsy Bear's experience of being cared for and protected from danger brings alive the sense of God's providing care in Psalm 23:

The LORD is my shepherd;
I have everything I need.
He lets me rest in fields of green grass
and leads me to quiet pools of fresh water.
He gives me new strength.
He guides me in the right paths,
as he has promised.
Even if I go through the deepest darkness,
I will not be afraid, LORD,
for you are with me.
Your shepherd's rod and staff protect me.
Psalm 23. 1-4

The following questions suggest further ways of developing the links between the young child's experience, the story and the Bible passage.

Talk about going for walks:
Where do you like to go walking?
Who do you like to go walking with?
Who do you meet when you go walking?
Have you ever got lost or hurt yourself when you were
out for a walk? What happened? Who looked after you?

Talk about the story:
Where did Betsy Bear go walking?
What did she see?
What did she do? Who did she meet?
How did she know she would be safe?

Think some more about the story:
Where else might Betsy Bear go walking?
What would she see? What would she do? Who would she meet?
How would she keep safe?

Explorer

Teddy Horsley wonders at God's Handiwork

Teddy Horsley is a bear who likes to go exploring.

He likes to explore the house where he lives.

Who puts his breakfast on the table in the morning?

Who brings clean clothes to his bedroom every week?

Who fixes the broken shelves in the kitchen?

Who mends the dripping tap in the bathroom?

Who mops the floor and dusts the furniture?

Everywhere he explores in the house, Teddy Horsley
sees signs of Mr and Mrs Henry's work and care.

Teddy Horsley likes to explore the garden where he lives.

Who waters the new plants peeping from the earth?

Who sweeps the leaves from the garden path?

Who paints the gate at the end of the garden?

Who pulls the weeds from the flower beds?

Who collects the rubbish to burn on the bonfire?

Everywhere he explores in the garden, Teddy Horsley sees
signs of Lucy and Walter's work and care.

Teddy Horsley likes to explore the world where he lives.

Who puts the sun in the morning sky?

Who lights the stars in the evening dark?

Who covers the rooftops with a carpet of snow?

Who brightens the grass with plants and flowers?

Who waters the earth with running rivers?

Everywhere he explores in the wide, wide world, Teddy Horsley sees signs of God's work and care.

In *The Explorer,* Teddy Horsley's discovery of signs of care around him as he explores his home brings alive the sense of the world as God's handiwork and Job's experience of wonder and awe in Job 38:

The Lord spoke to Job.

Were you there when I made the world?

Who decided how large it would be?
Who stretched the measuring-line over it?
Do you know all the answers?

Do you know where the light comes from
or what the source of darkness is?

Have you ever visited the storerooms,
where I keep the snow and the hail?

Who dug a channel for the pouring rain
and cleared the way for the thunderstorm?
Who makes rain fall where no one lives?

Who waters the dry and thirsty land,
so that grass springs up?
Does either the rain or dew have a father?
Who is the mother of the ice and the frost,
which turn the waters to stone
and freeze the face of the sea?

Can you guide the stars season by season
and direct the Great and the Little Bear?

Who is it that feeds the ravens
when they wander about hungry,
when their young cry to me for food?
Job 38.1, 4a, 5, 19, 22, 25-30, 32, 41

The following questions suggest further ways of developing the links between the young child's experience, the story, and the Bible passage.

Talk about exploring and discovering things:
Where do you like to go exploring? What do you find?
What signs of work and care do you discover when you explore your house?
What signs of work and care do you discover when you explore your garden?

Talk about the story:
What did Teddy Horsley discover when he explored the house?
Who takes care of the house?
What did Teddy Horsley discover when he explored the garden?
Who takes care of the garden?
What did Teddy Horsley discover when he explored the world?
Who takes care of the world?

Think some more about the story:
Where else might Teddy Horsley go exploring?
What might he discover?
What signs of work and care might he find?

Think about the Bible passage:
Pretend you are exploring the places described in the passage.
Imagine you were exploring the sky. What might you discover?
Imagine you were exploring the earth. What might you discover?
What other signs of God's work and care can you discover in the world around you?
How would you answer some of God's questions to Job?

Neighbours

Betsy Bear helps her Neighbours

Betsy Bear likes to meet her neighbours.

She gets up early to see the dustman

and runs down the path to meet the postlady.

She calls to the woman next door hanging out her washing

and waves to the man down the road weeding his garden.

She watches the people waiting at the bus stop

and chats to her friends riding on the bus.

She plays with the children running in the park

and laughs with the babies sitting in their prams.

She pushes her trolley round the supermarket
and smiles at the shoppers waiting at the checkout.

Whoever she meets in the wide, wide world Betsy Bear knows
they are all her neighbours.

Betsy Bear likes to help her neighbours.

She picks up some waste paper for the dustman.

She opens the garden gate for the postlady

and carries the pegs for the woman hanging out her washing.

She fetches the water for the man weeding his garden

and looks after a bag for a mother at the bus stop.

She gives up her seat for an old man on the bus

and pushes a girl on the swing at the park.

She cheers up a baby crying in his pushchair.

She unloads her shopping at the checkout and helps the man
pack it in boxes.

Whoever she helps in the wide, wide world, Betsy Bear knows they are all her neighbours.

In *Neighbours,* Betsy Bear's experience of meeting and helping her neighbours bring alive the Great Commandment of Luke 10:

A teacher of the Law came up and tried to trap Jesus. "Teacher," he asked, "what must I do to receive eternal life?" Jesus answered him,"What do the Scriptures say? How do you interpret them?" The man answered, "'Love the Lord your God with all your heart, with all your soul, with all your strength, and with all your mind'; and 'Love your neighbour as you love yourself'."
"You are right," Jesus replied; "do this and you will live."
But the teacher of the Law wanted to justify himself, so he asked Jesus, "Who is my neighbour?"
Luke 10.25-29.

The following questions suggest further ways of developing the links between the young child's experience, the story, and the Bible passage.

Talk about meeting and helping neighbours:
Who are your neighbours?
When do you meet them?
Where do you meet them?
How do you help them?

Think some more about the story:
What other neighbours might Betsy Bear meet?
When would she meet them?
Where would she meet them?
How would she help them?

Talk about the story:
Who were Betsy Bear's neighbours?
When did she meet them?
Where did she meet them?
How did she help them?

Think about the Bible passage:
How do you love?
How do you show you love for them?
How do people show love for their neighbours?
How would you answer the teacher's final question to Jesus?

Also available in this series: A Day with Teddy Horsley:
Good Morning   The Grumpy Day   Night Time